Shopping

PORIRUA LANGUAGE PROJECT
with ARLA Federation of Aotearoa NZ Inc.
and Whitireia Publishing

First published in 1993 by the Porirua Language Project,
12 Hartham Place, Porirua
and
ARLA Federation of Aotearoa NZ Inc.

1994 Edition : AVANTI BOOKS
8 Parsons Green
Boulton Road
Stevenage SG1 4QG

Edited by Ruth Munro, Shelley Whittaker, Rodney Strong
Illustrated by Janelle Barker
Designed by Sarah Maxey, Daphne Brasell Associates Press

ISBN 1-898614-03-2

Today is Benefit day.

We are going shopping.

We catch the bus to the Centre.

We go to Countdown.

We buy Weetbix, bananas, and sausages.

We buy bread and milk.

We buy a new toothbrush for Tom.

We get to the checkout.

Tom is crying.

Where is the toothbrush?

We go and look.

Here it is!

Tom is happy.

Tom likes his toothbrush!